Contents

Mrs Fairborn's baby

Mrs Rapunzel Fairborn had a lot to be thankful for. She had the long, golden hair that had always been in her family. She had a good man, Mr Alistair Fairborn, and she had a job. She had to wash and sweep up hair in the top celebrity hair salon, 'Tumbling Tresses'.

But she adored children and longed for a child of her own to love.

"Do not despair!" said Mr Fairborn. "We will have a child one day and she will have your long, golden hair!"

One hectic day in the 'Tumbling Tresses' hair salon, a wizened old gran, with just a few strands of hair left on her bony skull, snuck in for a trim. She sat herself in the top celebrity sparkly chair. (It was only ever sat upon by celeb of celebs, DJ Cool Kat.) Rapunzel was sweeping up hair, the hairdressers were snipping, gelling and spraying and not one of them spotted her – oops!

A blast of cold air hit the salon and in swept Cool Kat.

"Hair. Sort it. Pronto!" she bellowed.

Whipping off her dark glasses, Cool Kat click-clacked in her high heels to *her* chair. Then she let out the screech of a lost prairie dog. It hung in mid-air.

"What is that *thing* in *my* chair? Get up, you old fool!"

She had a flair for being fairly dramatic.

Mrs Rapunzel Fairborn had a soft spot not just for children, but for old folk too. She forgot who she was. She forgot the salon boss. She had seen Cool Kat being unfair before, but this was too much… Rapunzel Fairborn flipped!

"Who do you think you are? Goldilocks? You haven't got the hair for it!" Rapunzel yelled. "You don't need a hairdo. You need some respect! This lady's staying in the celebrity chair!"

Well! Cool Kat fell off her high heels in shock. The salon boss didn't know if he wanted to sob or clap. But the old gran had something to say to Mrs Fairborn.

"You are strong and bold to stand up to such a bully. I want to repay you. Tell me, what do you and your husband wish for most of all?"

Maybe it wasn't magic, because this is no fairy story, but soon after, Ricky Alistair Patrick Unzel Fairborn was born with long (very long), golden hair. His mum sighed with bliss as old grans peeped into the pram and said, "All that golden hair! Isn't *she* sweet?"

Not even magic always gets it right ...

It's **football** – but not as we know it!

Handball! Penalty! **Yessss!**

If you play football, it helps to understand the rules. Maybe you do (or think you do). But the rule book looked a lot different back in the 1860s …

At first, each part of the country had its own set of firm rules. To be fair they split each match in two, playing first by one team's set of rules, and then by the other. That's why matches today are still played in two halves.

Some rules from back then may seem a bit odd to us today …

Teams must meet before the match to agree on:

- how long the pitch will be
- how long the match will last
- how many men will be on each team
- what sort of ball to play with.

A player may not pick the ball up, but he can catch the ball and run with it.

To shoot he must drop the ball first.

If a player is holding the ball, another player can kick him, grab at his shirt or strangle him!

A player may push the goalkeeper into the dirt.

Some dirty players might have spikes on the bottom of their boots. Ouch! This would stir the players up. Men had to be strong and hard to play football. Women didn't play football until the 1900s.

You may not pass the ball forwards. As in rugby, you must pass to a man behind you.

Poor fans – they might wait all day for a goal! Best change the rules and play that the first team to score wins – if you can see the ball in the dark of night!

Shirts shall have no names on them and may be any colour.

So to tell if a man is on your team, you'd need to look at the colour of his cap!

Two refs will be on the pitch, each twirling a flag. They must agree if a goal has been scored.

Goals have no nets, and maybe just string for a crossbar! The refs cannot send a player off, or even twirl their flags for a foul – players in the 1800s were too fair not to follow the rules. Just like today, right?

Christmas 1914

In 1914, Britain was at war with Germany. They were fighting in France. They fought from trenches with land in the middle known as no-man's-land. This letter, from a man who was there on Christmas Day 1914, shows an account of the first Christmas of the war.

27th December 1914   France

Dearest Father,

As your son, I wish I could have spent Christmas with you and Mother in our old house back in England, but as a soldier, I was proud to be with my Tommy pals. Today there has been a lot of shelling from the Germans and I should be snatching a bit of sleep, but I am scribbling this by candlelight as I sit in my cold dug-out. I want to tell you about the astonishing events of Christmas Day in the middle of no-man's-land.

It was a freezing, dark night on 24th December. The moon was out but its light was hidden by the clouds of dust and mud high in the air. The sounds that night were of men shouting, rounds of bullets and screeching shells. No-man's-land, in between ours and the Fritz's (German) trenches, was full of crouching shadows and black, scorched trees as we kept fighting for a little more ground. That seems to be what this war is about – just a bit of ground!

We had no chance to think about Christmas Day, but in between the fighting, we hung candles on tree branches.

The next morning, 25th December, was oddly quiet. The Germans had also hung candles and they had put trimmings, cut from scraps, on a little fir tree.

It was a misty Christmas morning and we were up to our knees in mud in our freezing dug-outs. We had parcels from loved ones and the Red Cross and split the gifts between us. I got a pair of thick, woollen socks and a tin of beef!

We hung around, expecting the sound of pounding guns and shells to wreck the stillness. When would the first shot ring out?

Well, it wasn't a shot that rung out but the sound of German soldiers singing Christmas carols!

We found ourselves stepping into no-man's-land to meet with the German soldiers. We shook hands and passed round food and drink with the men we had been ordered to kill.

Then it happened. Someone found a football! Without fuss, we formed teams. Worn out from weeks of fighting, we still found the strength to play on the frozen ground. No ref. Just helmets for goals. We slipped and skidded about in our big, muddy boots, and I tackled a German and kicked the ball to score! The Germans played well too. In the end, it was 3−2 to them, but we were *all* men and players to be proud of.

The true spirit of Christmas was in that truce and I'll be proud to tell my own children about it one day.

Well, the candle has gone out and I must sleep. Tell Mother I missed her Christmas cooking.

Your son,

Alfred

Unwrap – and enjoy!

Listen up, boys and girls! Shout if you enjoy chocolate!

Lots of voices! OK, that's all of you! But what do you know about this scrummy sweet?

The story of chocolate

Chocolate comes from cocoa beans grown in very hot parts of West Africa and South America. Long ago, the Mayas from South Mexico used the beans as cash, swapping them for other objects. Then they started to boil the beans and drink the liquid. The Aztecs followed the Mayas, and they called this liquid 'xocolatl' (or 'tchocolatl') – bitter water. The spoiled King Montezuma drank it from a gold cup!

Then in 1519 the Spanish explorer, Cortes, went to Mexico and found – chocolate!

In 1657 chocolate houses started opening in London, serving chocolate mixed with water or milk. They were very popular. Chocolate was here to stay!

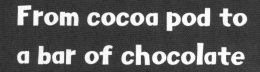

From cocoa pod to a bar of chocolate

Pull off the foil, open your mouth – and enjoy! You won't be disappointed. But how did your chocolate bar get here?

First, the cocoa pods are harvested.

Then the pods are left out in the hot sun.

The rest happens in a noisy factory, and lots of staff are employed to do it. The beans are scooped out of the pods, which are destroyed. Then the beans are cooked and ground into a thick, dark liquid with a strong smell – in a good way!

The liquid is sweetened and milk may be added.

It is stirred until it is smooth. And there you have it – chocolate!

But how is this turned into chocolate bars and sweets?

There are three ways:

1. For solid bars, the liquid chocolate is tipped into trays and cooled.

2. For filled bars, the hard fillings are set out on a conveyor belt and liquid chocolate is tipped over them. The filled bars are left to cool.

3. For chocolates with soft fillings or toys in them, the liquid is tipped into hollow pockets and cooled. Then the fillings are added and the bits are stuck together with chocolate.

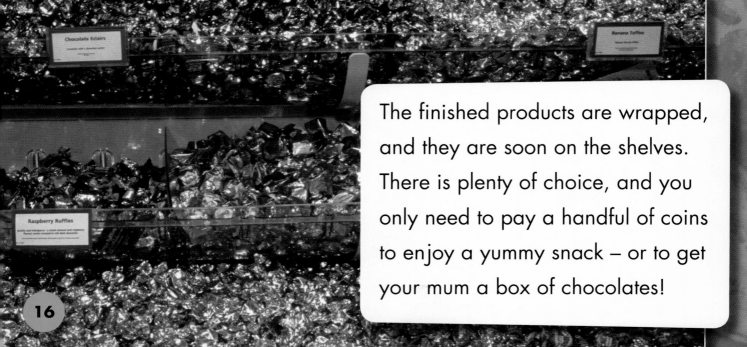

The finished products are wrapped, and they are soon on the shelves. There is plenty of choice, and you only need to pay a handful of coins to enjoy a yummy snack – or to get your mum a box of chocolates!

Did you know that ...

- The first bar of chocolate was formed by Fry's in 1847.

- Dark chocolate is the king of chocolate – and a small helping is good for us!

- You need about 80 cocoa beans for just one 100 gram chocolate bar.

- This will annoy your pooch, but chocolate is poisonous to dogs – avoid feeding it to them!

- The largest bar of chocolate was formed in Armenia in 2010 – it was a massive 4 tonnes!

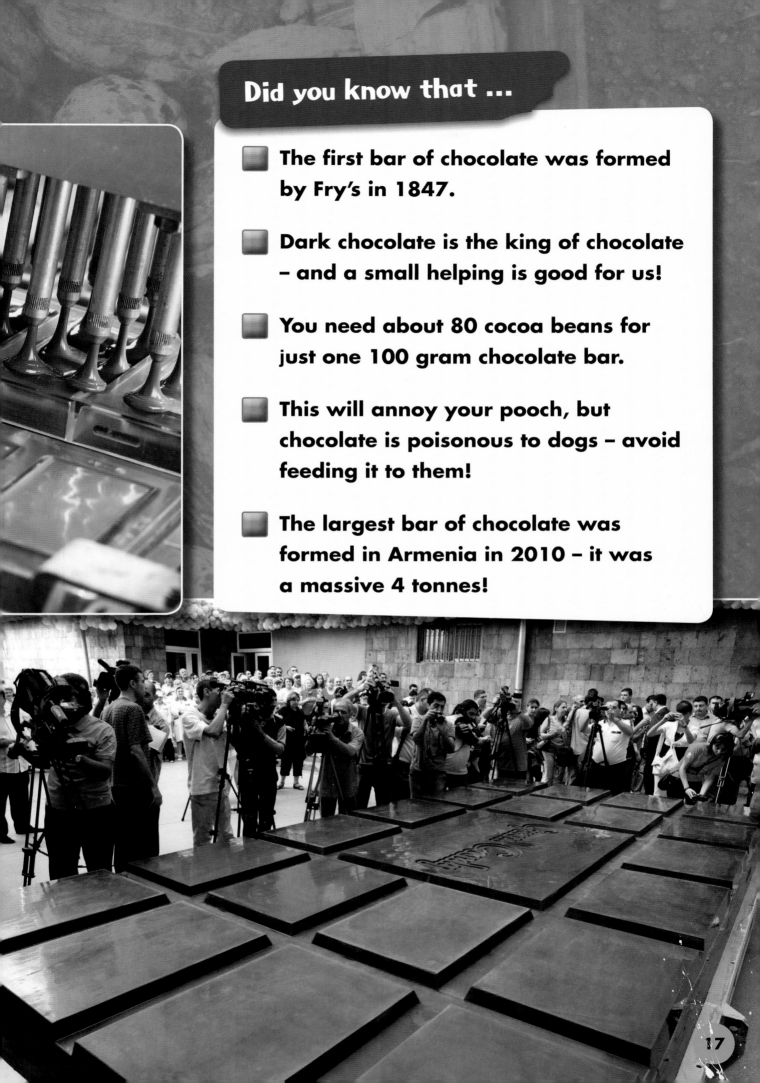

Get your skates on!

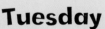

Mrs Fairborn's baby (air)

Green words: *Say the sounds. Say the word.*

h<u>air</u>   ch <u>air</u>   <u>air</u>   mid-<u>air</u>   fl<u>air</u>

Say the syllables. Say the word.

F<u>air</u>'born → F<u>air</u>born   Al'is't<u>air</u> → Alist<u>air</u>   des'p<u>air</u> → desp<u>air</u>   h<u>air</u>'dress'ers → h<u>air</u>dress ers
f<u>air</u>'ly → f<u>air</u>ly   un'f<u>air</u> → unf<u>air</u>   h<u>air</u>'do → h<u>air</u>do   f<u>air</u>'y → f<u>air</u>y

Red words:

to   be*   <u>she</u>*   <u>the</u>   of   do   s<u>ai</u>d   we   <u>one</u>   <u>your</u>   old*   h<u>er</u>   was   by*
w<u>ha</u>t   <u>you</u>   bef<u>ore</u>   <u>who</u>   <u>are</u>   som<u>e</u>   he*   want   a<u>ll</u>

Challenge words:

baby   golden   wa<u>sh</u>   <u>ch</u>ild   lo<u>ve</u>   bony   ever   ge<u>lli</u>ng   pronto   pr<u>air</u> <u>ie</u>   f<u>ol</u>k
Goldilo<u>cks</u>   lady   magic   bec<u>au</u>se   ĕven

Vocabulary check: **tresses** *long hair*   **adored** *loved*   **despair** *lose hope*

pronto *immediately*   **prairie dog** *a rodent, usually found in North America*

It's football – but not as we know it! (ir)

Green words: *Say the sounds. Say the word.*   f<u>ir</u>st   f<u>ir</u>m   <u>sh</u> <u>ir</u>t   st<u>ir</u>

Say the syllables. Say the word.

<u>th</u> <u>ir</u>st'y → <u>th</u> <u>ir</u>sty   <u>th</u> <u>ir</u>t'y → <u>th</u> <u>ir</u>ty   St<u>ir</u>'ling Stirling

Say the root word. Say the whole word.

d<u>ir</u>t → d<u>ir</u>ty   tw<u>ir</u>l → tw<u>ir</u>l<u>ing</u>

Red words:

we*   <u>you</u>   to   <u>the</u>   do   <u>th</u>ey   one   o<u>th</u>er   why*   <u>are</u>   som<u>e</u>   how   w<u>ha</u>t
<u>th</u>eir   would   so*   w<u>ere</u>

Challenge words:

understand   rûles   diff<u>er</u>ent   e<u>a</u><u>ch</u>   c<u>ou</u>ntry   t<u>ea</u>m   h<u>a</u>l<u>ve</u>s   ball   pl<u>ay</u> er
spîkes   women   behind   g<u>oa</u>l   change   nâmes   col<u>our</u>   f<u>ou</u>l   lîke

Vocabulary check: **crossbar** *horizontal bar between two upright posts of a goal*

* These words are red for a while.

Christmas 1914 (ou)

Green words: *Say the sounds. Say the word.*

our   house   proud   out   clouds   sounds   rounds   ground   found

Say the syllables. Say the word.   acc'ount → account   a'round → around

Say the root word. Say the whole word.

shout → shouting   crouch → crouching   pound → pounding

Red words:

was   they   were   who   there   of   the   father   your   son   could   you
mother   old*   my*   should   be*   want   to   what   we*   no   ones   would   all

Challenge words:

Christmas   Britain   war   Germany   fought   letter   December   dearest   soldier
cold   loved   ordered   teams   goals   players   true   truce

Vocabulary check: **trenches** *deep ditches where soldiers lived in the First World War*
Tommy *English soldier*   **shells** *missiles containing explosives*   **Red Cross** *a charity*
pounding *hammering, thumping sounds*   **truce** *an agreement not to fight*

Unwrap – and enjoy! (oy oi)

Green words: *Say the sounds. Say the word.*

boys   voices   boil   foil   toys   choice   coins

Say the syllables. Say the word.

en'joy → enjoy   dis'a'pp'oint'ed → disappointed   noi'sy → noisy
em'ploy'ed → employed   des'troy'ed → destroyed   ann'oy → annoy
poi'son'ous → poisonous   a'void → avoid

Red words:

all   you   what   do   comes   the   other   they   water   was   your   here   are
of   to   there   by*   small

Challenge words:

chocolate   cocoa   beans   Mexico   swapping   bitter   Montezuma   gold   explorer
opening   serving   turned   conveyor   together   only   Fry's   tonnes

Vocabulary check: **harvested** *to pick crops*   **ground** *crushed into small pieces*

24

These words are red for a while.